Tom's B
Treat

Written by John Priest
Illustrated by Jamie Smith

Heinemann

Chapter 1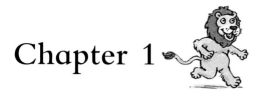

Tom jumped out of bed. He pulled on his jeans and a T-shirt. It was his birthday. He was eight years old.

He ran downstairs and into the kitchen.

'Happy birthday, Tom,' said his mum. 'Eat your breakfast quickly. Dad has had his breakfast and he wants to make an early start.'

Tom's dad was taking Tom and two of his friends to the zoo for a birthday treat.

'When you get back it will be time for your party,' said Mum.

'Yippee!' said Tom.

After breakfast, Tom and his dad got into the car. They picked up Sally and Robbie and set off for the zoo.

On the way to the zoo, Tom's dad stopped outside a large shop.

'Why have we stopped here?' asked Tom.

'Don't worry, this won't take long,' said Dad. 'I thought you'd like to have a look round a fancy dress shop. You can all choose a costume to wear at the party this afternoon.'

Inside the shop, Tom, Sally and Robbie looked at all the costumes.

'Wow!' they said.

Sally tried on a clown's costume. She put on a large orange wig and a big red nose. Everyone laughed.

'Look at me!' said Robbie, 'I'm a robot!' Robbie was wearing a shiny silver costume. It had little coloured buttons and switches on it. He pressed the buttons and flicked the switches. The red, yellow and blue lights on his helmet started flashing. He looked just like a robot.

Tom had chosen an astronaut's costume. It had a helmet with a visor. Tom lifted the visor and said, 'Greetings Earthlings!'

Sally and Robbie laughed. 'You look great!' they said.

Tom wanted to show his dad their costumes. They looked round the shop but they couldn't see him.

Suddenly, Tom's dad jumped out from behind a curtain.

'ROOARR!' he growled.

'Yeeow!' screamed Sally.

'Don't worry, Sally,' said Tom. 'It's only my dad in a lion's costume playing a trick on us. Please can we keep the costumes on, Dad? We want to wear them to the zoo.'

'Okay,' said Dad, 'I'll wear mine too.'

At the zoo, there were all sorts of animals to look at and there were exciting fun-fair rides to go on as well.

'What shall we do first?' asked Tom.

'I like seeing all the animals,' said Dad, 'but I'm not so sure about going on those wild rides.'

'Oh, Dad,' said Tom, 'you always say that but you do like them really.'

9

They decided to look round the zoo first. They went to see the gorillas, then the monkeys. Afterwards, they watched the giraffes eating leaves from tall trees.

Then they went to the sea lion pool and watched the sea lions being fed. When the zookeeper heard that it was Tom's birthday, she let him hold out a fish for one of the sea lions. The sea lion swallowed the fish in one mouthful.

Then Robbie said, 'Look! The whale show is just about to start.'

Chapter 2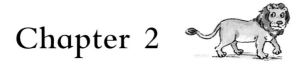

They sat next to a massive pool.
A great big black and white whale
was swimming in it. They watched
him dive down to the bottom of
the pool. Then the whale shot up,
straight out of the water. When
he landed, he made a loud
SPLOSH! The water splashed
over everyone. Tom's dad
was soaked.

'I'm dripping wet!' cried Dad. 'I'll have to get a towel from the car. Wait here until I get back.'

On the way back to the car, Tom's dad heard one of the zoo-keepers using a loudhailer and he saw a large crowd of people standing listening. The zoo-keeper was saying, 'I don't want to alarm anyone, but one of our lions has escaped. Please make your way to the fun-fair. It's the safest place to be.'

The crowd of people hurried off towards the fun-fair.

'Oh, dear!' said Tom's dad. 'I'd better get back to the children right away.'

He was just about to set off for the whale pool when he was surrounded by zoo-keepers. They threw a big net over him. He tried to get free, but the net held him tight. He tried to call out, but his lion's nose was stuck through a hole in the net and he couldn't open his mouth.

Tom and his friends were getting fed up waiting.

Tom looked at his watch. 'What can Dad be doing?'

'Let's go and look for him,' Tom said. Tom, Sally and Robbie walked towards the car park.

Then Sally saw something lying in the grass. She whispered to Tom, 'Look over there. I think I can see a lion in the long grass.'

The three children crept nearer. They could see a long, yellow tail, waving in the air.

'It can't be a real lion,' said Tom. 'I bet it's my dad playing a trick on us again!'

'Let's scare him this time!' Sally said.

They crawled through the grass.

'One! Two! Three! GO!' shouted Tom, and the three children jumped on to the lion's back.

The lion let out a loud roar.

ROOOARRRR!

Robbie squeezed the lion's big nose. 'It's no use. You can't scare us!'

The lion growled again.

Tom pulled its whiskers. 'Come on, Dad. You're coming on the fun-fair rides with us.'

All three children held the lion by its long, golden mane and pulled him towards the fun-fair.

When they reached the fun-fair, lots of people saw the lion and ran away.

'It's all right,' Tom said. 'It's only my dad.' The people still ran away.

'Let's go on the waltzer first, then the roller coaster,' said Robbie.

They watched the waltzer spin round and round, faster and faster.

'Car number seven looks the fastest,' said Tom. 'Let's get in that one.'

When it stopped they climbed in and the lion let out a loud growl.

'Don't be frightened, Dad,' said Tom. 'You'll enjoy this ride.'

When the lion opened his mouth again, they saw his long, sharp teeth.

'Dad!' said Tom 'It's rude to yawn like that!' And he closed the lion's mouth with his hands.

'Dad gets nervous before a ride,' Tom said to his friends. 'You'll have to help me get him into the waltzer.'

So Tom and Sally held the lion's mane, and Robbie grabbed his long tail and gave it a good tug. The lion jumped up into the waltzer.

He didn't look at all happy.

'Don't worry, Dad. You'll be okay,' said Tom.

The waltzer twisted and turned. By the time it stopped, all the children were dizzy. The lion's legs were knocking together and he couldn't stop shaking.

'Your dad is really funny!' said Robbie.

'This is a great birthday treat!' said Tom.

Chapter 3

'Now let's go on the roller coaster!' Robbie shouted.

They stood by the roller coaster. The cars went really fast. They were faster than the waltzers. When the lion saw it, his eyes rolled and he went cross-eyed. He tried to creep away.

'Oh no you don't, Dad!' said Tom, grabbing his tail.

The three children pushed the
lion into one of the cars.

The cars started to climb the
track. They went high into the
air, then, suddenly, they dropped
down a steep slope.

'Yahhooo!' Tom shouted.

'Weeeeee!' Sally shouted.

'Yippeee!' Robbie shouted.

'Grrreeeoww! Oooowwwww!' the lion roared.

The cars went faster towards a big loop. They whizzed round the large circle, turning upside down first, then the right way up, then upside down again.

When the ride finished, the
children were laughing.

The lion looked terrified.

'Dad!' Tom shouted 'You've
dribbled all over my costume!'

Using one of the lion's heavy
paws, he wiped the lion's mouth.
'These gloves you're wearing are
dangerous, Dad,' said Tom, pulling
at the lion's paw. 'The claws are
much too sharp and pointed.
You'll have to be careful you
don't hurt someone.'

The lion yelped, shaking his
paw in the air.

'Which ride shall we go on now?' Sally asked.

'How about the big rocket that shoots you into the air?' said Robbie.

The lion shook his head. He let out another loud roar and ran off.

The children ran after him.

The lion ran past the giraffes. He ran past the whale's pool. The children still followed.

'Dad! Dad!' Tom called. 'If you don't want to go on the rocket, you can go back on the waltzer!'

But the lion kept on running. It ran past the crocodiles, and up to a big gate.

The sign on the gate said
BEWARE OF THE LIONS.
Quickly, the lion ran through the
open gate and slammed it shut.

Tom tried the gate. It was
locked. 'Dad, what have you
done?' he said. 'Now you're locked
in with the lions!'

BEWARE
OF THE
LION

Tom and his friends set off to find a zoo-keeper. They found the head zoo-keeper, sitting in a big office.

'Excuse me, please,' Tom said.

'What is it?' the zoo-keeper asked.

'My dad's locked himself in with the lions. Can you let him out please?'

The zoo-keeper smiled. 'Are
you sure THIS isn't your dad?'
He pointed at someone dressed
in a lion costume.

'Dad? Is that you?' asked Tom.

'Yes, it's me,' said Tom's dad.
'Where have you been? I've been
looking all over for you. This man
thought I was the lion that
escaped!'

'You mean...you haven't been on the waltzer with us?' asked Sally.

'No,' said Tom's dad.

'I suppose you didn't come on the roller coaster either...?' asked Robbie.

'No,' said Dad again.

'And you didn't run away from the rocket ride?' asked Tom, quietly.

'I don't know what you're talking about,' Dad said.

At that moment, another
zoo-keeper ran into the room.
'I've just seen the strangest
thing. The lion that escaped has
come back and let himself in!'

The children looked at
each other.

'That means...,' said Robbie,

'...that we've...,' said Sally,

'...been on the rides with a real
lion!' said the three children,
all together.

'What a scary birthday treat!'
said Tom.